Cap'n Alec Apostrophe

is known as The One-Eyed Punc because he wears a black patch...

...he's also the Wanderin' Punc who pops up all over the place, cuttin' down and shortenin' words.

He's skipper of what he calls a fishin' boat. He's brave and he's kind, but he's easily upset when he feels that people are what he calls

treatin' 'im 'urtfully

– just because he gabbles and slurs his words.

After his very first week at school,
Alec's teacher, Miss O'Puncley,
noticed that he had a squint.

"Oh dear," she thought,

"he'll have difficulty with
his lessons. I'll have to
tell his parents."

He doesn't take after me

Alec's mother wasn't surprised, as she'd noticed that he often looked at her sideways.

"I'll take him to the optician's,"

she said to her husband.

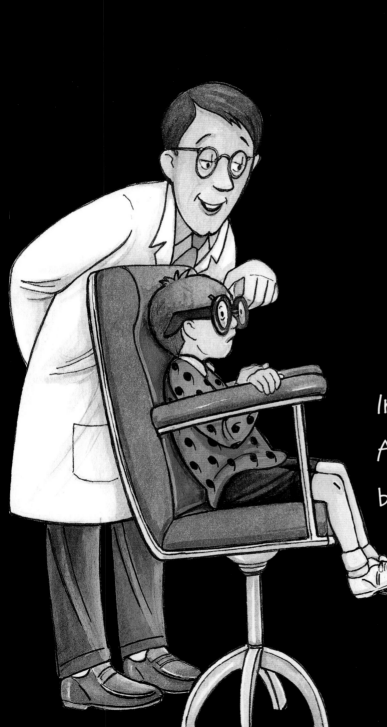

In next to no time, Alec's eyes were being tested by Mr Gaze of Puncspec's.

"He's suffering from a lazy eye," said Mr Gaze.

"He'll have to wear a patch over his good eye. It'll make his lazy eye work properly."

"Don't worry, m'boy," murmured Mr Gaze as he fitted a pink patch around Alec's head.

"This'll do the trick."

Because of the patch,
Alec couldn't
read very easily and he
wasn't able to write very well.
(That's why he's always spoken so
badly, droppin' 'is h's and 'is g's
and turnin' two words into one.)

But Alec wasn't too bothered by his
reading and writing, as he was

brilliant at what he called
’urdlin’ and
pole vaultin’.

Every year Alec's Greek father Aristotle and his Scottish mother Annie would take him to the seaside. One year they'd stay with the Apostrophes on the island of Apos; another year they'd visit Annie's family, the MacPuncs, on the Scottish coast.

As well as what he called learnin' deep-sea fishin' and sailin', Alec's favourite pastime was shell-collectin'.

The Apostrophes of Apos
(don't ever dare to call
them the Apostrophe's!)
weren't at all rich, but
they'd worked hard and built
themselves a swordfish boat
called Cyclops.

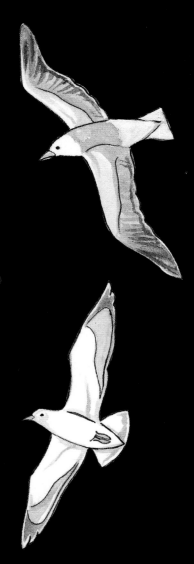

Alec's delight was sitting in
the crow's nest with his
telescope, looking out for what
he called the Big 'Uns.

When they stayed with the MacPuncs (don't ask for trouble by calling them the MacPunc's!), Alec, Ari and Annie didn't spend much time at what Alec called messin' about in boats. Instead, they'd put on their Tam o' Shanters and their waders and go salmon fishin' in the nearby river.

In case you're worrying about Alec's eyesight, here's what happened.

One morning, he rushed into his parents' bedroom and told them that

'e'd been lookin' at 'imself in the mirror – and 'e'd noticed that 'e wasn't squintin' anymore. Mr Gaze's patch 'ad done the trick!

You'd have thought that Alec would've been glad to be without his patch, but after a few days he'd started to miss it. So he made up his mind that when he was older he'd go to sea, wearing a patch like his great-grandfather Cap'n Athos Apostrophe, the famous pirate known as **Blackpunc**.

As you'll have learned by now,
the sea's in Alec's blood.
So it wasn't long before
he'd left home, put on his
black patch, and found a job.

"I'll do anythin'," he said:
"mendin' nets, sewin' sails,
cleanin' fish."

He worked day and night, and he'd
soon bought himself a boat.

Alec's crew were two local lads whom
he called 'enry and 'erbert.
While Alec was at the wheel,
they'd be flinging out
the nets and hauling in
the fish, watched by
the ship's cat, Appie.

"What's in the bag today?" Alec would ask, as he peered at what he called 'eaps of 'errin's and 'addock wrigglin' on the deck.

Alec's Band o' Brothers

Alec now has a bigger boat,
called The Jolly Punc,
and – as you'll have guessed –
a bigger crew.

"I 'and-picked 'em at
the Puncport Job Shop,"
said Alec.

"They're a mixed bunch,
but it's a very 'appy ship."

When he's not at sea, Alec lives with Appie and his parrot, Nipper, in a cottage only a stone's throw from the harbour.

"I'll never get married,"
he growls.

"Who'd put up with an 'usband who's always wanderin' around the world smellin' of fish?"

Puttin' in apostrophes

You've (you have) probably worked out by now that Alec wouldn't (would not) have been the way 'e (he) is if 'e hadn't (had not) been born with a squint.
He wouldn't be droppin' (dropping) 'is (his) h's and his g's. He'd only be in words where the Apostrophes belong (as in **Alec's parrot**). What makes him angry is seeing himself where he doesn't (does not) belong (like in Pickled Whelk's and Jellied Eel's).
So when you are reading or writing something, please keep a careful eye on Alec's apostrophes!

Alec's Checklist

- **Apostrophes take the place of missing letters. You should put an apostrophe where the missed out letter would go, like this:**
  I'm (I am), he'll (he will), who's (who is), didn't (did not), could've (could have), can't (cannot), it's (it is)

- **Use an apostrophe for belonging words, like these:**
  The pirate's parrot **(add 's to singular words...)**
  Athos's eyepatch **(...even if the word ends in an s)**
  The pirates' treasure **(add 's to plural words that end in s...)**
  The crew's boat **(...and also to those that don't)**
  Alec's great-grandfather's ship **(add 's to the end of hyphenated words, too)**
  Ari and Annie's cat **(add 's to the last name to show the cat belongs to both of them)**

- **Some names already have an apostrophe in them:**
  Miss O'Puncley (surnames)
  Puncspec's (shop names)
  Alec wears a Tam o' Shanter

- **Apostrophes are used in dates where some numbers have been left out:**
  '60 (1960)

- **Use an apostrophe to record the time, like this:**
  It's 9 o'clock in the morning
  (o' means 'of the')

- **Remember:** it's means it is. Never use an apostrophe in the belonging word **its** (Alec's boat is on **its** way)